Siliciclastic Sequence Stratigraphy in Well Logs, Cores, and Outcrops: Concepts for High–Resolution Correlation of Time and Facies

Siliciclastic Sequence Stratigraphy in Well Logs, Cores, and Outcrops: Concepts for High-Resolution Correlation of Time and Facies

by

J.C. Van Wagoner, R.M. Mitchum,
K.M. Campion, and V.D. Rahmanian

AAPG Methods in Exploration Series, No. 7

Published by
The American Association of Petroleum Geologists
Tulsa, Oklahoma 74101 U.S.A.

Published 1990
Second Printing 1991
Third Printing 1992
Fourth Printing 1996

ISBN: 0-89181-657-7

Association Editor: Kevin T. Biddle
Science Director: Richard Steinmetz
Publications Manager: Kenneth M. Wolgemuth
Special Projects Editor: Anne H. Thomas
Copy Editor: William G. Brownfield

This and other AAPG publications are available from:
The AAPG Bookstore
P.O. Box 979
Tulsa, OK 74101-0979
Telephone: (918) 584-2555; (800) 364-AAPG (USA— book orders only)
FAX: (918) 560-2652

Table of Contents

venation, downward shift in coastal onlap, or onlap of overlying strata; it may be marked by local erosion due to fluvial processes and local evidence of subaerial exposure such as soil or root horizons normally found in coastal-plain deposits. The correlative surface on the shelf is a conformable surface with no significant hiatus indicated and is marked by thin pelagic or hemipelagic deposits. These deposits include thin carbonates, organic-rich mudstones, glauconites, and volcanic ashes indicating terrigenous-sediment starvation. Strata across correlative surfaces usually do not indicate a change in water depth; commonly the correlative surfaces in the coastal plain or on the shelf can be identified only by correlating updip or downdip from a marine-flooding surface. In even deeper-water environments, such as the slope or basin floor, parasequence boundaries may also be unrecognizable.

The characteristics of parasequence boundaries suggest that they form in response to an abrupt increase in water depth that is sufficiently rapid to overcome deposition. The stages of parasequence-boundary formation are simplistically illustrated in Figure 4.

In two special cases, shown in Figure 5, parasequences may be bounded either above or below by sequence boundaries. In the first case (Figure 5, Example 1), a sequence boundary truncates a parasequence in the underlying transgressive systems tract and erodes into lower-shoreface sandstones (well A) and marine mudstones (well B). Subsequent deposition of a lowstand-shoreline parasequence on top of the sequence boundary results in (1) a younger parasequence bounded above by a marine-flooding surface and below by a sequence boundary, and (2) an older parasequence bounded below by a marine-flooding surface and above by an erosional sequence boundary. The correct parasequence interpretation in Example 1, based on recognition of the sequence boundary, is contrasted in Figure 5 with the incorrect parasequence interpretation that results if the sequence boundary is not identified.

In the second case (Figure 5, Example 2) the sequence boundary in well 2, expressed as a surface of subaerial exposure, coincides with a marine-flooding surface. This juxtaposition of surfaces results in a parasequence bounded above by a sequence boundary and below by a marine-flooding surface. There are three coincident surfaces at the top of the youngest parasequence in well 2: (1) the marine-flooding surface originally bounding the parasequence, probably formed at the end of the highstand, (2) the sequence boundary, expressed as a subaerial exposure surface, and (3) the last marine-flooding surface formed during the sea-level rise that terminated the lowstand.

Parasequence boundaries, within a framework of regional sequence boundaries, are the best surfaces to use for *local* correlation of time and facies from logs and cores, and as surfaces on which paleogeographic maps can be made, for several reasons. (1) Parasequence boundaries are easily recognizable surfaces that separate older beds from younger beds. (2) The boundaries form rapidly (similar observations have been made by other authors, notably Wilson, 1975; and Goodwin and Anderson, 1985), probably within hundreds of years to thousands of years, and approximate time markers useful for chronostratigraphy (Sears et al., 1941; Krumbein and Sloss, 1963; Wilson, 1975; Goodwin and Anderson, 1985). (3) Parasequence boundaries bound genetically related assemblages of facies, providing an essential framework for facies interpretation and correlation on well-log cross sections within the sequence. (4) Finally, they commonly are areally extensive enough for local subsurface correlation within a basin. However, parasequence boundaries usually cannot be easily correlated regionally with widely spaced well control. For this reason, and because parasequence distribution is very sensitive to sediment supply, parasequence boundaries usually are not good surfaces for regional correlation of time and facies.

Vertical Facies Relationships in Parasequences

Well-exposed outcrops in the Blackhawk Formation of east-central Utah were studied to document the vertical and lateral facies relationships in parasequences as a guide for subsurface correlation. These exposures also have been studied by Spieker (1949), Young (1955), Balsely and Horne (1980), Kamola and Howard (1985), and Swift et al. (1987). To relate outcrop observations of parasequences to subsurface expression, three wells were drilled on the outcrop by Exxon Production Research Company in 1982. Each well was cored and logged continuously with a suite of conventional electric- and nuclear-logging tools. The vertical facies relationships of parasequences from the Late Cretaceous age (Campanian) Blackhawk Formation are shown in Figure 6 in outcrop, core, and well log, the latter from one of the nearby 1982 wells. Each parasequence on the log is marked by an upward decrease in gamma-ray response, indicating an upward increase in the sandstone/mudstone ratio within the parasequence and generally an upward increase in the sandstone bed or bedset thickness. This vertical pattern of upward coarsening and thickening reflects parasequence progradation.

Each parasequence boundary in Figure 6 is marked by a blue line on the well log. The parasequence from interval A (160 to 218 ft, or 49 to 66 m) begins at the base with interbedded mudstones and burrowed, hummocky-bedded sandstones deposited in the lower shoreface of a beach. The upper part of the cored interval consists of trough and tabular cross-bedded sandstones and planar-laminated sandstones deposited, respectively, in the upper shoreface and fore-

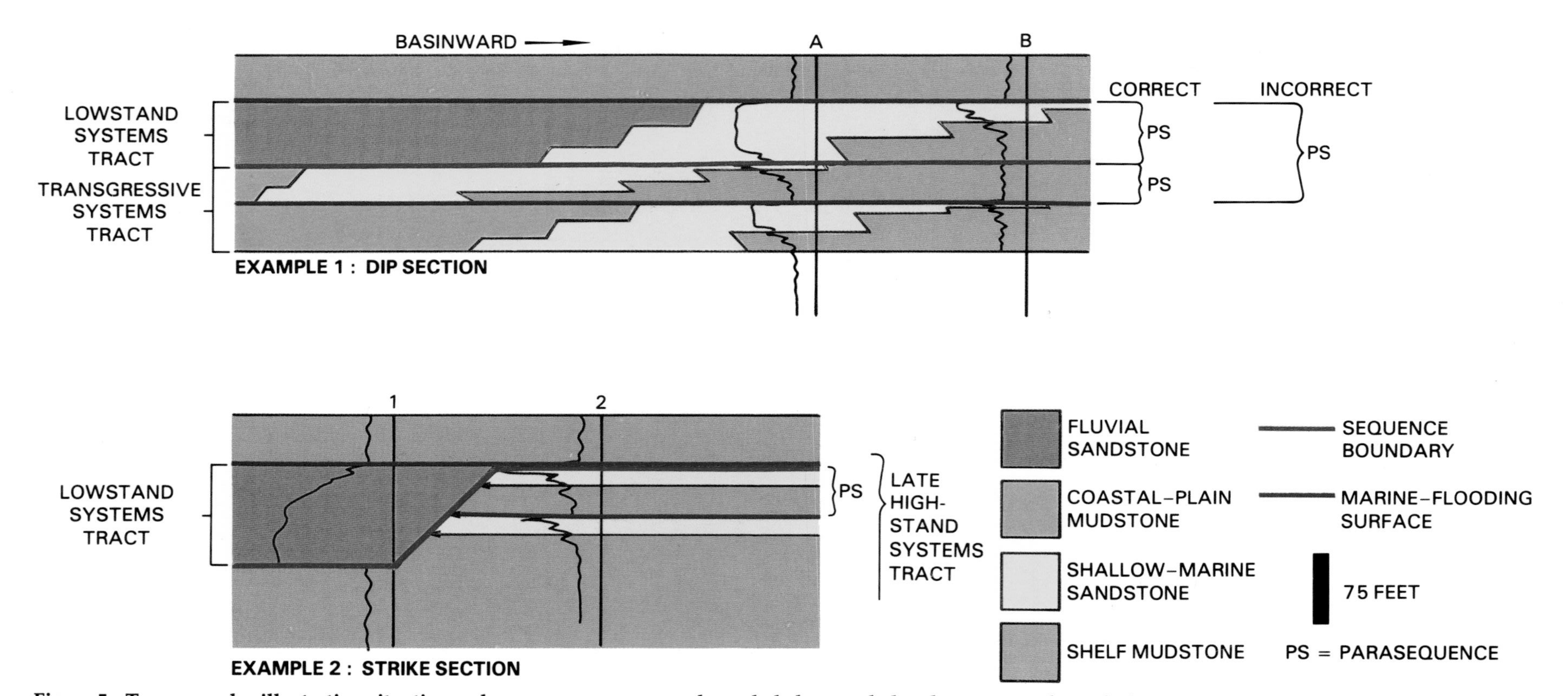

Figure 5—Two examples illustrating situations where parasequences are bounded above or below by sequence boundaries.
Example 1—If a sequence boundary occurs between two marine-flooding surfaces, as illustrated in well B, the parasequences are defined from sequence boundary to flooding surface (illustrated as "correct"), and not from flooding surface to flooding surface (illustrated as "incorrect").
Example 2—A marine-flooding surface bounding the youngest parasequence in the highstand systems tract is often coincident with a sequence boundary. In well 2 the parasequence boundary is coincident with a sequence boundary.

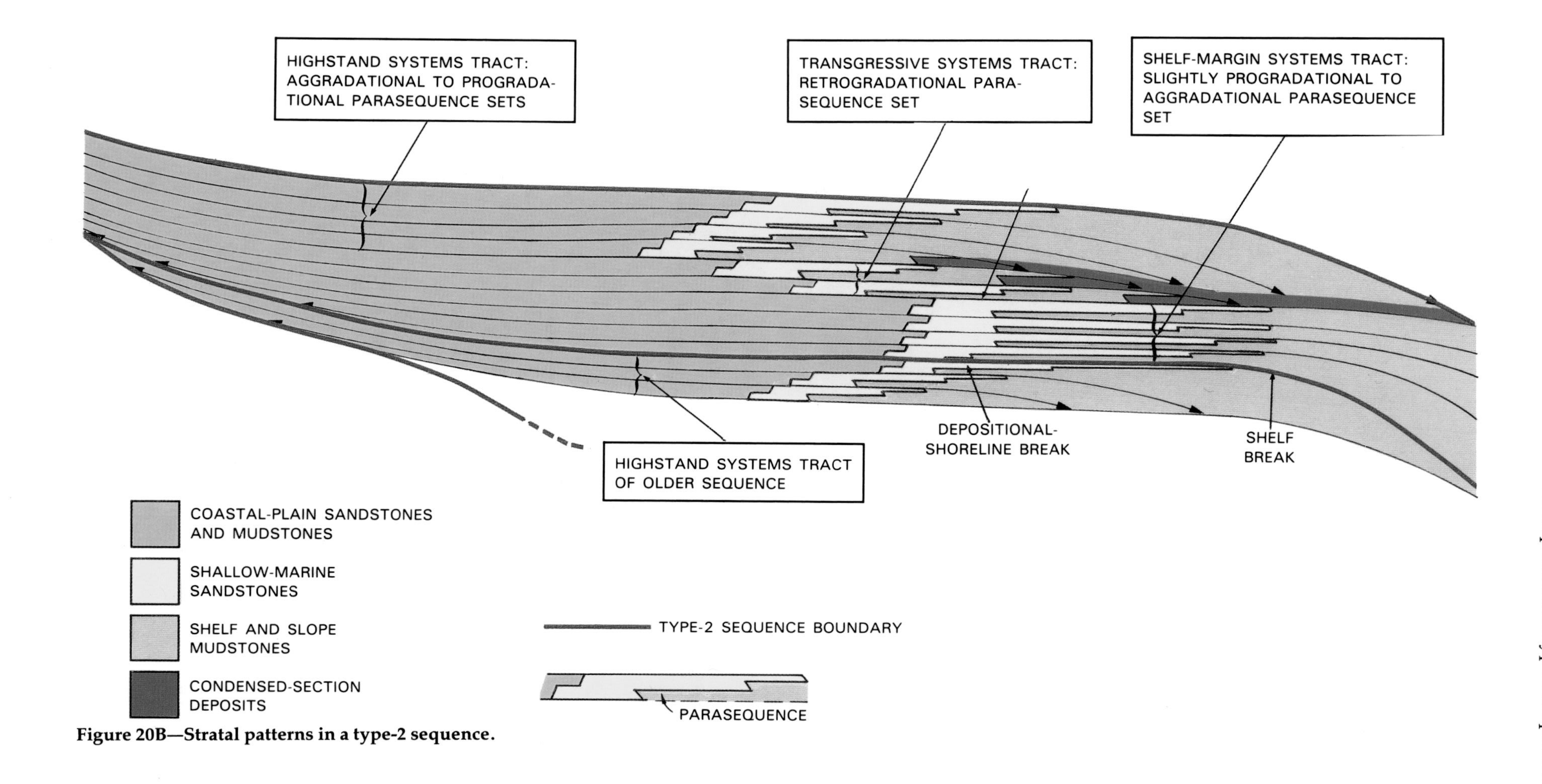

Figure 20B—Stratal patterns in a type-2 sequence.

parasequence sets composed of shallow-marine parasequences with updip coastal-plain deposits. The base of the shelf-margin systems tract is the type-2 sequence boundary, and the top is the first significant flooding surface on the shelf. The transgressive and highstand systems tracts in type-2 and type-1 sequences are similar.

Type-2 sequences (Figure 20B) and type-1 sequences deposited on a ramp (Figure 20A) superficially resemble each other; both lack fans and canyons, and both of their initial systems tracts (shelf-margin systems tract in the type-2 sequence and lowstand systems tract in the type-1 sequence) are deposited on the shelf. However, unlike the type-1 sequences deposited on ramps, there is no relative fall in sea level at the depositional-shoreline break for the type-2 sequence. Consequently, type-2 sequences do not have incised valleys and they lack the significant erosional truncation that results from stream rejuvenation and a basinward shift in facies.

Sequence Boundary Characteristics

A sequence boundary is an unconformity and its correlative conformity; it is a laterally continuous, widespread surface covering at least an entire basin and seems to occur synchronously in many basins around the world (Vail et al., 1977; Vail and Todd, 1981; Vail et al., 1984; Haq et al., 1988). A sequence boundary separates all of the strata below the boundary from all of the strata above the boundary (Mitchum, 1977) and has chronostratigraphic significance. Correlation of sequence boundaries on well-log cross sections provides a high-resolution chronostratigraphic framework for facies analysis. If sufficient well control is available, not only does this framework equal or surpass other tools in chronostratigraphic resolution, but, if necessary, the framework can be developed from the well-log data base. The following discussion of sequence boundaries is divided into three parts: recognition criteria, incised-valley attributes and examples, and correlation pitfalls.

Recognition Criteria

The criteria that identify the unconformable part of sequence boundaries in a *single* well log, core, or outcrop include a basinward shift in facies for a type-1 sequence boundary and a vertical change in parasequence stacking patterns for a type-1 or a type-2 sequence boundary. As an example of the latter criterion, consider the case of three parasequence sets arranged in vertical order from the oldest to the youngest: retrogradational, progradational (or aggradational), followed by retrogradational. In this case, there is commonly a sequence boundary at the top or the base of the progradational (or aggradational) parasequence set.

On a well-log or outcrop *cross section* the recognition criteria for the unconformable part of a type-2 sequence boundary include onlap of overlying strata, a downward shift in coastal onlap, and subaerial exposure with minor subaerial truncation, all landward of the depositional-shoreline break within the updip, coastal-plain part of the sequence where correlation is less precise. For this reason, these criteria are particularly difficult to recognize in well-log or outcrop cross sections. Type-2 sequence boundaries are most readily defined by the changes in parasequence stacking patterns described above. Based on this criterion, type-2 sequence boundaries in siliciclastic strata appear to be rare in most basins.

On a well-log or outcrop cross section the recognition criteria for the unconformable part of a type-1 sequence boundary include the following:

- Subaerial-erosional truncation, a laterally correlative subaerial-exposure surface marked by soil or root horizons, and laterally correlative-submarine erosion, especially in the deep-water slope environment must be present.
- Onlap of overlying strata either onto the margins of incised valleys or coastal onlap must exist.
- A downward shift in coastal onlap (Vail et al., 1977); however, this commonly cannot be demonstrated on well-log cross sections because much of the coastal onlap occurs in the updip, fluvial part of the sequence where accurate well-log correlation is difficult, and therefore, the criterion of a basinward shift in facies must be used.
- To confirm that erosional truncation and a basinward shift in facies marks a sequence boundary and not a local-distributary channel, one or more of these criteria must be demonstrated over a regionally significant area.

The unconformable part of a type-1 sequence boundary can be traced seaward into a conformable surface on the shelf or slope, commonly occurring at or near the base of a marine parasequence. Based on the criteria listed above, applied to the stratigraphic analysis of many basins around the world, type-1 sequence boundaries appear to predominate in siliciclastic strata.

Not all of the recognition criteria presented above occur everywhere along a particular type-1 sequence boundary in a basin. A type-1 sequence boundary has different physical expressions depending on where it is observed and on the variations along a basin margin in rates of sediment supply and sea-level change.

On the slope, seaward of the shelf break or in deeper-water environments, the most pronounced attributes of a type-1 sequence boundary are truncation and onlap. The distribution of these recognition criteria is controlled by the distribution of submarine canyons, slope failure, contour-current erosion set up by lowstand conditions, and the deposition of the basin-floor and slope fans.

of a basin with rivers carrying little or no bed load and a moderate to rapid rate of relative sea-level rise will be marked by truncation and widespread soil or root horizons or equivalent evidence of subaerial exposure, if preserved, but not by a basinward shift in facies. The sequence boundary would not be recognized in an individual well log and probably not recognized in cores. However, correlation demonstrating truncation of resistivity markers on well-log cross sections or seismic lines would readily reveal the incised valley and sequence boundary.

Finally, a type-1 sequence boundary in a basin or a portion of a basin with no rivers will be marked only by widespread evidence of subaerial exposure, if this evidence is not removed by the subsequent sea-level rise. A thin transgressive lag of calcareous nodules lying on the flooded sequence boundary is commonly the only indication that a soil horizon existed on the sequence boundary before the sea-level rise. This lag is discussed in more detail in the section "Parasequence Boundary Characteristics" and more briefly discussed at the end of this section. Significant erosion and a basinward shift in facies will not be associated with the sequence boundary in this case. The sequence boundary will probably not be recognized in a well log in the absence of core, and might be only recognized in the well if it were correlated from another area where it was more clearly expressed.

In Figure 26, different expressions of the type-1 sequence boundary on the shelf or ramp are labelled SB1 where they are beneath sandstone-filled incised valleys; SB2 where they are beneath shale-filled incised valleys; and SB3 to show where the sequence boundary is conformable on the shelf or ramp seaward of the lowstand shoreline. Marine-flooding surfaces marking parasequence boundaries are labelled FS, and subaerially exposed interfluves marking the sequence boundary away from the incised valleys coincident with the flooding surface are labelled FS/SB. Depositional environments, stratal terminations, and other diagnostic criteria associated with type-1 sequence boundaries in siliciclastic strata on a shelf or ramp are summarized in the table in Figure 26.

In addition to the criteria listed in the table in Figure 26, sequence boundaries can be marked by various types of lag deposits. These lags include:

(1) transgressive lags of calcarous nodules deposited on marine-flooding surfaces that are coincident with sequence boundaries (FS/SB) or on sequence boundaries within incised valleys. The calcareous nodules are derived by shoreface erosion from soil horizons formed during the subaerial exposure of the sequence boundary.

(2) organic or inorganic carbonates deposited on marine-flooding surfaces that are coincident with sequence boundaries.

(3) basal-channel lags deposited on sequence boundaries within incised valleys.

The first two types of lags are discussed in the section "Parasequence Boundary." The third type of lag forms during sea-level fall as the shelf is eroded by fluvial channels forming the incised valleys. During incision, finer-grained shelf sediments are flushed through the valley system. Coarser-grained particles eroded from the shelf strata are concentrated as a basal lag as much as several feet thick on the sequence boundary in the valley. The lag derived from the shelf strata commonly consists of a wide variety of grain types including intertidal and open-marine shells, shark teeth, glauconite, phosphorite pebbles, shale rip-up clasts, and bones. The lag commonly shows evidence of subaerial exposure.

Basal-channel lags also may be derived from more proximal sources. These lags commonly consist of coarse grains of chert and quartz, well-rounded quartz and quartzite pebbles, and sandstone and shale rip-up clasts. It is common to find quartz and quartzite pebbles ranging in thickness from thin beds, only one pebble thick, to beds 1 or 2 ft (0.3 or 0.6 m) thick. Thin pebble beds may be deposited in the axes of incised valleys or at the edges of incised valleys, almost on valley interfluves. Commonly, basal-channel lags within valley axes consist of a mixture of particles derived from the incised shelf and more proximal sources. If the incised valley erodes into inner-shelf parasequences and the valley is filled with marine mudstones, or fine-grained estuarine or lower-shoreface strata, the basal-channel lag could be interpreted as transgressive lag with no apparent evidence of a relative fall in sea level. If the incised valley erodes into middle- or outer-shelf mudstones and the valley subsequently is filled with cross-bedded estuarine sandstones, the basal-channel lag could be interpreted as a transgressive lag overlain by a shelf-ridge sandstone.

In Figure 26, the sequence boundary between incised valleys (labelled FS/SB) is a soil or root horizon lying on a shallow-marine parasequence. This parasequence may be deposited during either the highstand systems tract of the previous sequence or the early part of the lowstand systems tract to which the incised valleys belong in Figure 26. The latter case probably occurs frequently in the rock record, forming in the following way. In the early stages of the relative fall in sea level, fluvial systems incise and move progressively seaward across the shelf as the shelf is exposed. Sediment eroded from the underlying highstand strata by the incised valleys is deposited seaward of and adjacent to the valley mouths, forming thin delta and beach parasequences. As the sea-level fall continues and incised valleys erode farther across the shelf, (1) new beach and delta parasequences are deposited farther out on the shelf at the mouths of incised valleys, (2) previously deposited parasequences are eroded in front of incised valleys or are partially to totally preserved and "stranded" on the shelf at the edges of, or adjacent to, the incised valleys, and (3) the "stranded" parasequences are overridden by the subaerial-exposure surface of the sequence boundary.

These "stranded" lowstand parasequences represent early lowstand systems tract deposition on the shelf or ramp. In basins with a shelf break, these parasequences could predate submarine-fan deposition before the sea-level fall reaches the shelf edge. Although they form during the early part of the sea-level fall, they are overlain by a regionally extensive unconformity marked by subaerial exposure and truncation labelled on Figure 26 as SB1, SB2, SB3, and FS/SB. Although it does not record the time of the initial sea-level fall over its entire extent, this unconformity is the sequence boundary because (1) it separates all of the rocks below from the rocks above; (2) although all points on the surface do not represent the same duration of time, one instant of time is common to all points when the sea-level fall ends and the unconformity is completely formed; (3) it is readily identified over most of its extent; (4) it is the surface that controls the distribution of overlying strata in the lowstand systems tract on the shelf; and (5) it forms relatively quickly, probably in less than 10,000 years.

The "stranded" lowstand parasequences below the sequence boundary commonly have the following stratal characteristics:

(1) they typically are deltaic or beach parasequences, but commonly consist of sharp-based, lower-shoreface sandstones;
(2) they have no significant updip coastal-plain equivalents, and there is no sediment accommodation updip because of the sea-level fall;
(3) they rest, commonly abruptly, on open-marine strata, although their bases cannot be interpreted as a basinward shift in facies;
(4) they rest on a conformable surface, and each parasequence gradually shoals upward;
(5) they are overlain by the unconformable part of the sequence boundary marked either by minor truncation or subaerial exposure; and
(6) they generally are thin because of reduced accommodation on the shelf; their thicknesses typically do not exceed tens of feet; and they also may vary in thickness due to a varying amount of truncation below the overlying sequence boundary.

Paleovalley distribution on the shelf is often controlled by tectonic features such as basement-involved faults, thrusts, and growth faults. Structural lows caused by salt withdrawal also control valley distribution. In many cases, the paleovalleys deposited in low areas controlled by tectonics or salt are incised and can properly be called incised valleys. In other cases, especially when the topography created by the tectonics or salt is not subdued, the paleovalleys have little or no truncation at their bases. When little or no truncation exists, the sequence boundary is still marked by a basinward shift in facies at the base of the paleovalley fill, but the paleovalley cannot properly be described as incised.

Correlation Pitfalls

To interpret type-1 sequence boundaries correctly in well logs, cores, or outcrops, it is critical to distinguish between incised valleys and local channels, such as distributary channels, in constructing an accurate chronostratigraphic framework. In the examples presented in Figures 21 through 25, we interpreted the vertical association of facies on the cross sections as incised valleys and not distributary channels or other local channels because the valleys are too wide to be distributary channels, the strata at the edges of the incised valleys are distal-marine sandstones and shelf mudstones, not delta-front or stream-mouth bar deposits, and valley fills occur along certain surfaces, i.e., sequence boundaries, that are widespread in the basin and not confined to one deltaic lobe. Criteria for the differentiation of incised valleys from distributary channels in a single well log and on a well-log cross section or in an outcrop are explained more fully in the following paragraphs.

Incised-valley interpretation is more difficult in a single well log than on a cross section because distributary channels, eroding deeply into underlying deltaic deposits, can juxtapose relatively coarse-grained strata directly on prodelta mudstones thereby mimicking a basinward shift in facies. However, where a distributary channel of a given delta lobe cuts into but not through the prodelta mudstones of the same lobe, the thickness of the distributary-channel fill cannot be much greater than the paleowater depth of the eroded mudstones. For example, if prodelta mudstones were deposited in 100 ft (30 m) of water, the fill of the distributary channel eroding into them must be nearly 100 ft (30 m) thick. This is not necessarily the case with incised valleys. Because incised valleys erode in response to a relative fall in sea level, the paleowater depth of the eroded mudstones beneath the sequence boundary is commonly much greater than the thickness of the valley fill. For example, shelf mudstones deposited in 300 ft (92 m) of water can be truncated by an incised valley only 30 ft (9 m) thick or less. As important as this relationship is, it is not always possible to determine accurately the paleowater depth of the strata imaged on a well log. Cores, cuttings, or an outcrop, if available, may provide enough data to interpret the paleowater depth.

Another important distinction between distributary channels and incised valleys that may be recognized in a core or outcrop is that the sequence boundary at the base of an incised valley commonly shows evidence of

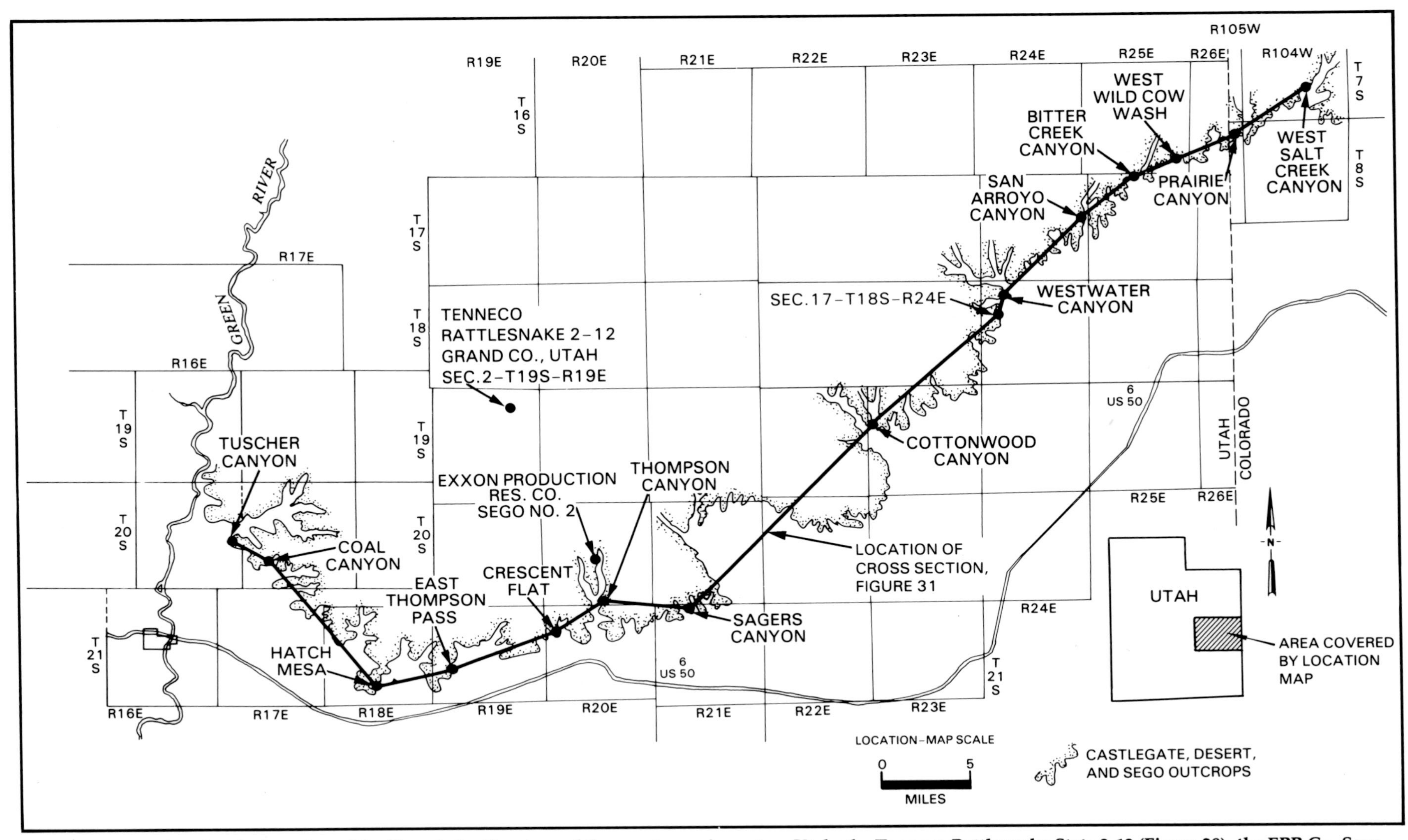

Figure 32—Map showing the location of the Desert, Castlegate, and Sego outcrops in eastern Utah, the Tenneco Rattlesnake State 2-12 (Figure 28), the EPR Co. Sego Canyon no. 2 (Figure 29), and the sequence cross section illustrated in Figure 31.

The lowstand systems tract of sequence 1 (Figure 33) consists of sandstones up to 250 ft (76 m) thick, characterized by a blocky to upward-fining SP well-log pattern. The sequence boundary at the base of the sandstones is a regional-erosional surface with local-erosional relief as great as 200 ft (61 m). The depositional environment of the sandstone is interpreted to have been fluvial or estuarine, filling a broad, incised-valley complex, based on log response and widely spaced core control. Maps constructed using the additional nine regional cross sections in the area show that the incised-valley complex is approximately 75 mi (120 km) wide. The depositional environment of the mudstones and thin sandstones below the sequence boundary is interpreted to have been middle to outer shelf, based on biostratigraphy and well-log responses. No intermediate water-depth deposits occur between the lowstand, incised-valley-fill sandstones and the underlying shelf mudstones of the previous sequence. Incised valleys of similar-aged sequences from Louisiana are illustrated in Figures 22 and 23.

The transgressive systems tract of sequence 1 (Figure 33) is composed of thin backstepping parasequences in a retrogradational parasequence set. A condensed section has not been identified in this systems tract. Only mudstones and very thin sandstones are preserved in the highstand systems tract. The coarser-grained part of the highstand systems tract apparently was truncated by the next sequence boundary. Erosion of the highstand systems tract by the overlying sequence boundary is common in many Tertiary sequences in the Gulf Coast basin. This pattern of systems tract distribution in sequence 1 is repeated in the other four sequences on the cross section.

The mudstone in the transgressive and highstand systems tracts is within the *Cibicides opima* shale. Based on the fauna in this shale, the lower sequence boundary on Figure 33 is dated as 15.5 Ma (L.C. Menconi, personal communication, 1989) and appears on the Exxon global-cycle chart of Haq et al. (1988). The youngest sequence in Figure 33 is within the *Bigenerina humblei* biozone and corresponds to the Hollywood sandstone, an informal regional mapping unit within this biozone, suggesting an age date of 14.7 Ma for sequence boundary 5 (L.C. Menconi, personal communication, 1989). Based on these age dates, each of the five sequences in Figure 33 is interpreted to have been deposited during sea-level cycles lasting 100,000 to 200,000 years. These frequencies may be even higher if one assumes a significant hiatus on the third-order boundary representing basin-floor and slope-fan deposition. A model for the development of these high-frequency sequences and their implications for the interpretation of eustasy as a driving mechanism for sequence development are the topics of the next section.

Interpretation of Depositional Mechanisms and Sequence Frequency

Sequences and their boundaries are interpreted to form in response to cycles of relative fall and rise of sea level. Jervey (1988) and Posamentier et al. (1988) presented an analysis of the interaction between eustasy (see figure 7, Posamentier and Vail, 1988) and basin subsidence that is interpreted to form sequence boundaries.

The interpreted relationship of stratal patterns to accommodation for a type-1 sequence with no significant incised-valley-fill deposition is shown in the block diagrams of Posamentier and Vail (1988, their figures 1 to 6). A variation of this idealized sequence, based on observations made in the Tertiary strata of the Gulf of Mexico, is shown in block diagrams in Figures 34 to 38 in this book. These block diagrams illustrate the successive evolution, over a period of 120,000 years, of a sequence similar to the sequences in Figure 33, with well-defined incised valleys and erosional truncation of the highstand systems tract. As the block diagrams illustrate, fluvial deposits within incised valleys are commonly coarse-grained, low-sinuosity channels reflecting slow rates of accommodation. Transgressive and early highstand-fluvial deposits are commonly finer-grained, high sinuosity channels and associated overbank strata reflecting high rates of accommodation. These two different fluvial-architectural patterns can be used as a guide to interpret sequences in totally nonmarine sections (Shanley and McCabe, 1989). A eustatic curve in the corner of each block diagram is color-coded to indicate the interpreted relationship of the systems tracts to eustasy. This eustatic curve is a graphic representation of the eustatic cycle of Jervey (1988), although at a higher frequency. Outcrop photographs illustrate the stratal characteristics of the facies that occur typically in each systems tract.

Parasequences and their boundaries also can be interpreted as responses to cycles of relative fall and rise of sea level. Sea-level cycles are classified by Vail et al. (1977) according to the duration of the cycle: third-order cycles, defined from fall to fall, have durations of 1 to 5 million years, fourth-order cycles have durations of hundreds of thousands of years. Following Vail et al. (1977) we assign to fifth-order cycles durations of tens of thousands of years. The relationship between this hierarchy of eustatic cycles, subsidence, and the deposition of sequences and parasequences is illustrated in Figure 39. In this figure, a third-order eustatic cycle (approximately one million years) is added to fourth-order cycles (approximately 120,000 years), and fifth-order cycles (approximately 50,000 years) to form a composite eustatic curve. Adding a total subsi-

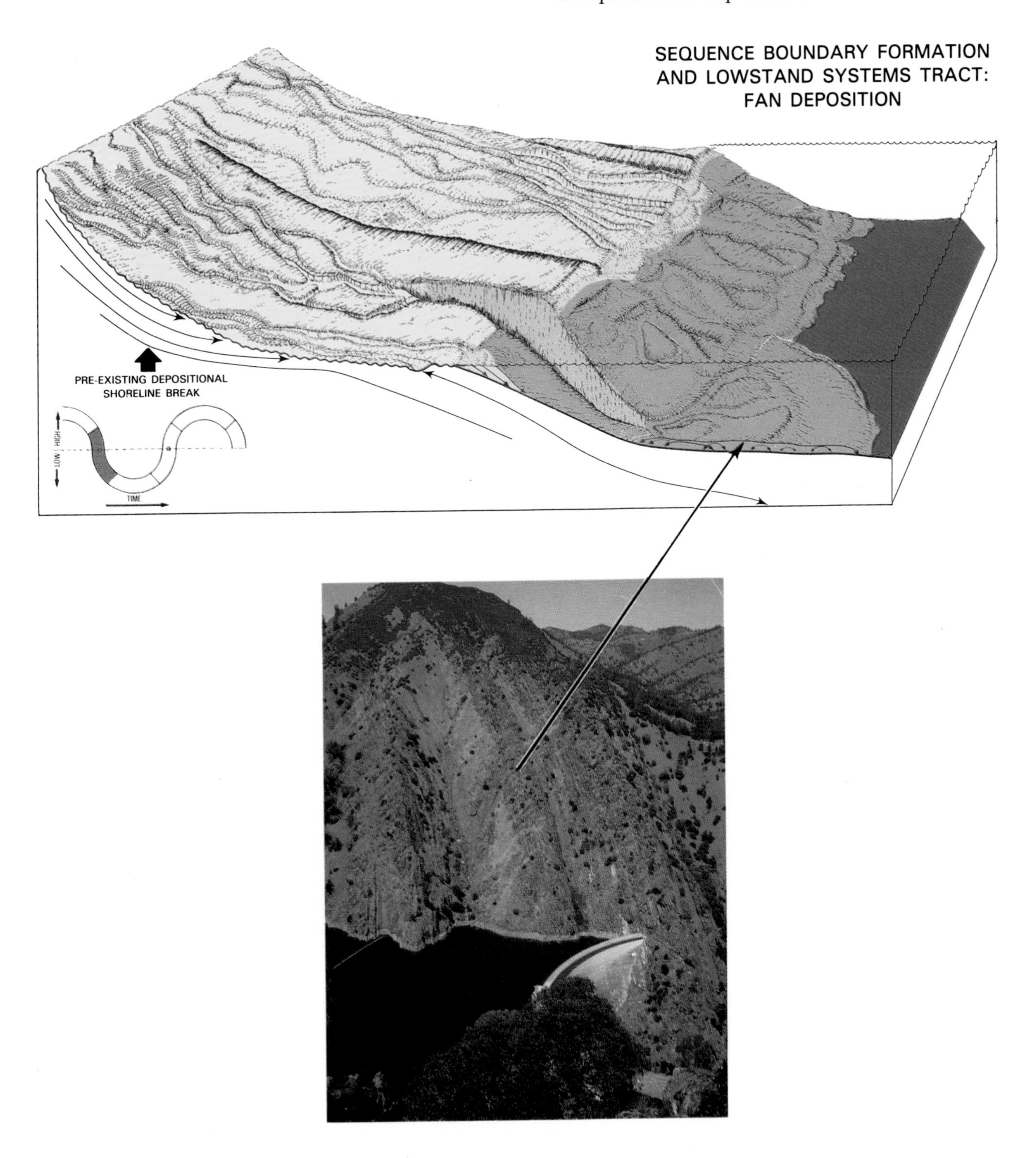

- RATE OF EUSTATIC FALL EXCEEDS RATE OF SUBSIDENCE
- SEA LEVEL FALLS TO SHELF BREAK, SHELF IS EXPOSED, INCISED; CANYON CUT
- SLOPE-PERCHED DELTAS AND SUBMARINE FANS ARE DEPOSITED

PHOTOGRAPH

SUBMARINE-FAN SANDSTONES; VENADO MEMBER, CORTINA FORMATION, TURONIAN, MONTICELLO DAM, CALIFORNIA

Figure 34—Sequence evolution: 1. Rapid relative fall of sea level.

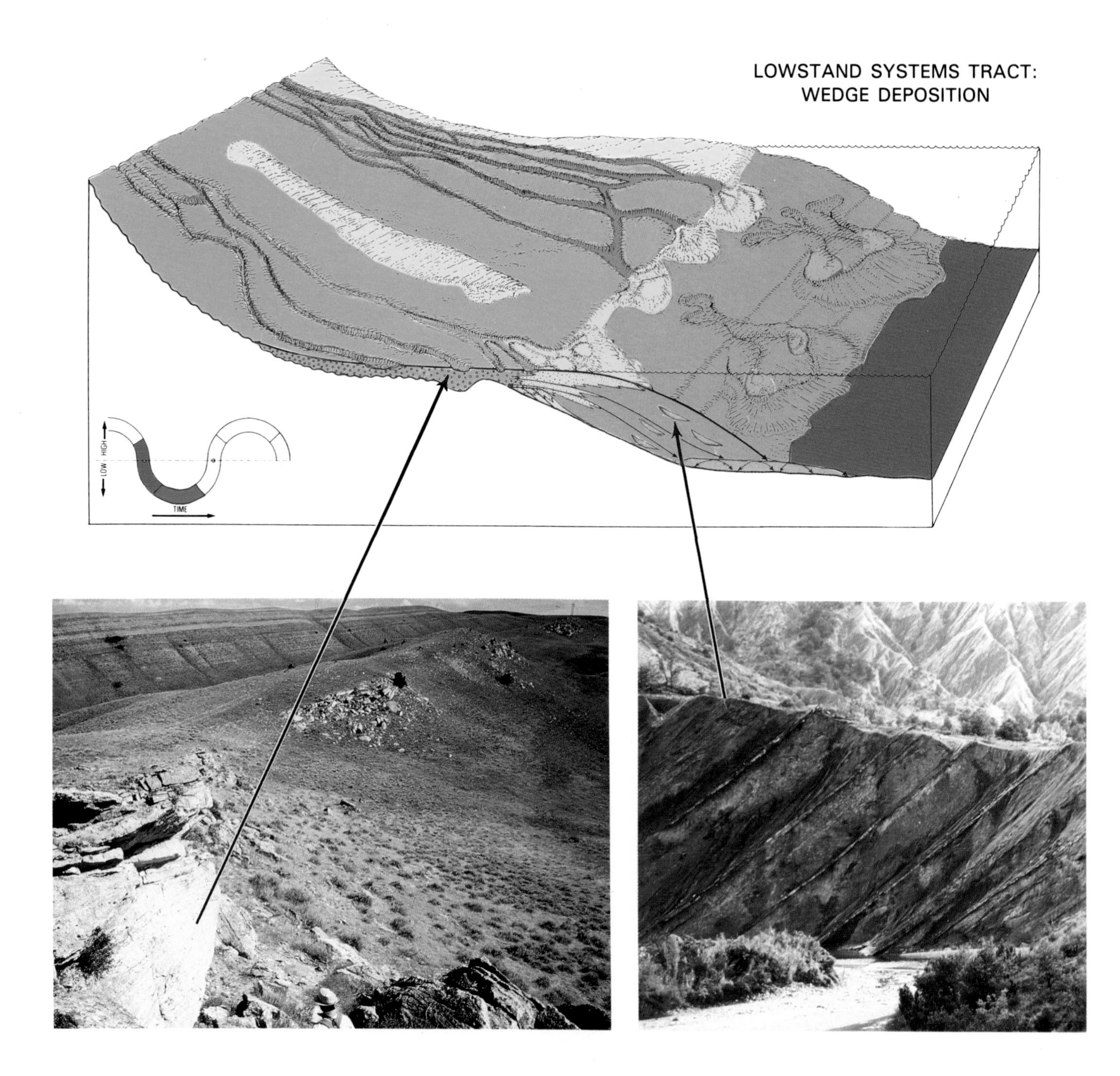

- RATE OF EUSTATIC FALL DECREASES, REACHES A STILLSTAND, AND RISES SLOWLY
- SUBMARINE-FAN DEPOSITION CEASES
- COARSE-GRAINED, BRAIDED-STREAM OR ESTUARINE SANDSTONES AGGRADE WITHIN THE FLUVIAL SYSTEMS OFTEN FILLING INCISED VALLEYS IN RESPONSE TO THE SEA-LEVEL RISE
- FINE-GRAINED TURBIDITES DEPOSITED ON THE SLOPE FORM A SHALE-PRONE WEDGE WITH THIN TURBIDITE SANDSTONE BEDS THAT DOWNLAP ON TOP OF THE FAN

PHOTOGRAPHS

LEFT: ESTUARINE INCISED-VALLEY FILL SANDSTONES; MUDDY SANDSTONE, WIND RIVER BASIN, WYOMING

RIGHT: LOWSTAND-WEDGE TURBIDITE SANDSTONES AND MUDSTONES, SPAIN

Figure 35—Sequence evolution: 2. Slow relative fall, stillstand, and slow relative rise of sea level.

- RATE OF EUSTATIC RISE IS AT A MAXIMUM
- DURING BRIEF SLOWDOWNS IN RATE OF RISE PARASEQUENCES PROGRADE BUT OVERALL STACK IN BACKSTEPPING PATTERN
- ORGANIC-RICH FACIES (CONDENSED SECTION) MOVES UP ONTO THE SHELF
- FLUVIAL SYSTEMS TYPICALLY SHIFT FROM A BRAIDED TO MEANDERING PATTERN

PHOTOGRAPHS

LEFT: RETROGRADATIONAL PARASEQUENCE SET, TRANSGRESSIVE SYSTEMS TRACT; TOP TEAPOT SANDSTONE, BIG HORN BASIN, WYOMING

RIGHT: BRAIDED-STREAM INCISED VALLEY-FILL SANDSTONE; TEAPOT SANDSTONE, BIG HORN BASIN, WYOMING

Figure 36—Sequence evolution: 3. Rapid rise of sea level.

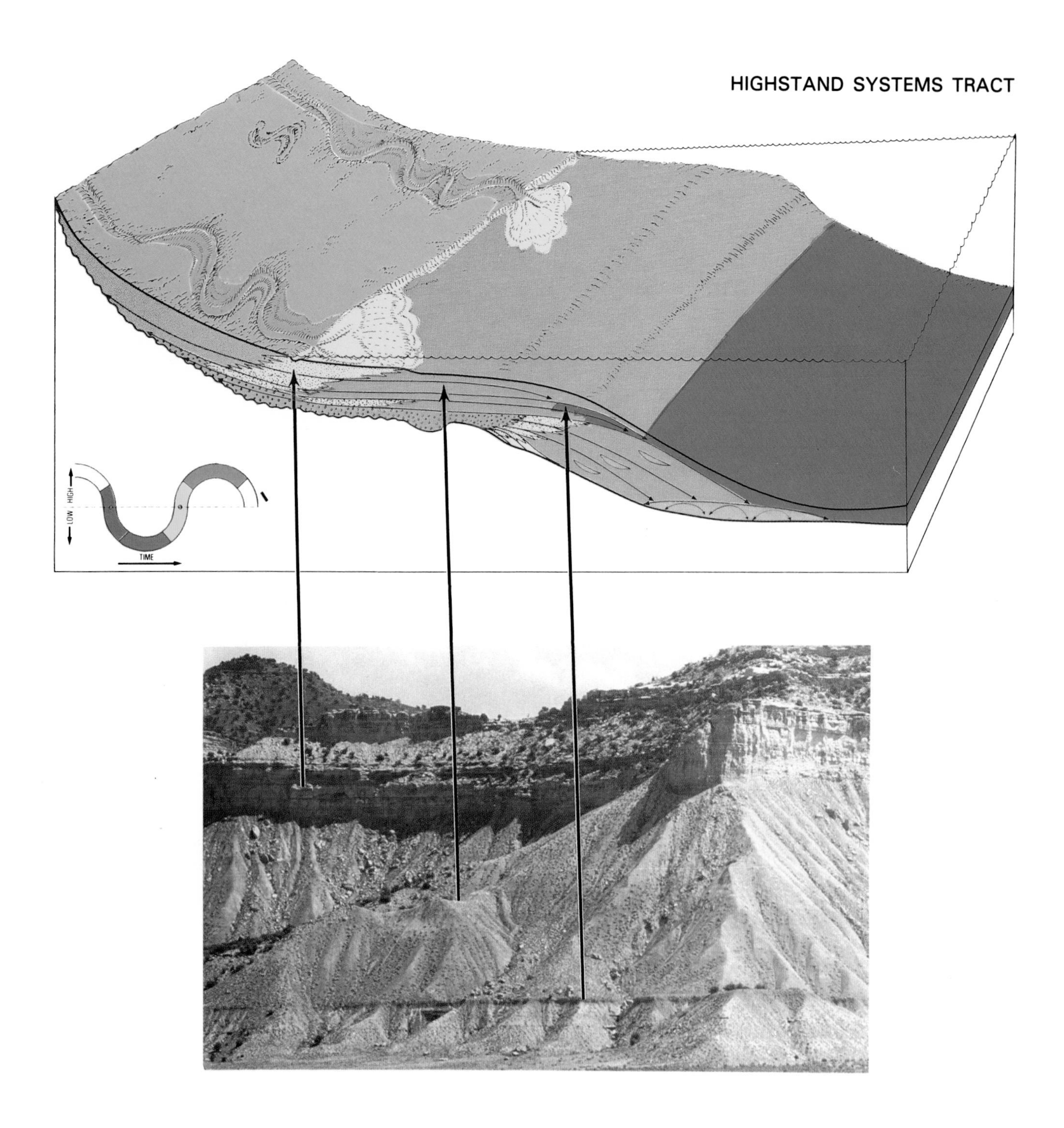

- RATE OF EUSTATIC RISE IS AT A MINIMUM AND IN THE LATE HIGHSTAND, FALLS SLOWLY
- RATES OF DEPOSITION GREATER THAN THE RATES OF SEA-LEVEL RISE, PARASEQUENCES BUILD BASINWARD IN AGGRADATIONAL TO PROGRADATIONAL PARASEQUENCE SETS OF THE HIGHSTAND SYSTEMS TRACT
- PARASEQUENCES DOWNLAP ONTO THE CONDENSED SECTION

PHOTOGRAPH

CONDENSED SECTION (PHOSPHATIC OOLITES) AND PROGRADATIONAL PARASEQUENCE SET, HIGHSTAND SYSTEMS TRACT; CASTLEGATE, BUCK TONGUE, AND SEGO MEMBERS, PRICE RIVER FORMATION, BOOK CLIFFS, DOUGLAS CREEK ARCH, COLORADO

Figure 37—Sequence evolution: 4. Slow relative rise, stillstand, and slow relative fall of sea level.

for relative fluctuations of sea level: Geology, v. 14, p. 617-620.
Cloetingh, S., 1988, Intraplate stresses: a tectonic cause for third-order cycles in apparent sea level?, *in* C.K. Wilgus et al., eds., Sea-level change: an integrated approach: Society of Econonic Paleontologists and Mineralogists Special Publication 42, p. 19-29.
DeGraw, H. M., 1975, The Pierre-Niobrara unconformity in western Nebraska, *in* W. G. E. Caldwell, ed., The Cretaceous system in the western interior of North America: Geological Association of Canada Special Publication 13, p. 589-606.
Dresser, H. W., 1974, Muddy Sandstone-Wind River basin: Wyoming Geological Association Earth Science Bulletin, v. 7, p. 5-70.
Dunbar, C. O., and J. Rogers, 1957, Principles of stratigraphy: New York, John Wiley and Sons, 356 p.
Duff, P. McL. D., A. Hallam, and E. K. Walton, 1967, Cyclic sedimentation: Developments in Sedimentology, v. 10, New York, Elsevier, 28 p.
Einsele, G., and A. Seilacher, eds., 1982, Cyclic and event stratification: New York, Springer-Verlag, 536 p.
Elliott, T., 1974, Abandonment facies of high-constructive lobate deltas, with an example from the Yoredale series: Proceedings of the Geologists Association, v. 85, part 3, p. 359-365.
Fisher, W. L., and J. H. McGowen, 1967, Depositional systems in the Wilcox Group of Texas and their relationship to occurrence of oil and gas: Transactions of the Gulf Coast Association of Geological Societies, v. 17, p. 105-125.
Fisk, H. N., 1944, Geological investigation of the alluvial valley of the lower Mississippi river: Vicksburg, Mississippi, U. S. Army Corps of Engineers, Mississippi River Commission, 78 p.
Fisk, H. N., 1961, Bar-finger sands of the Mississippi delta, *in* J. A. Peterson and J. C. Osmond, eds., Geometry of Sandstone Bodies: AAPG Special Publication, p. 29-52.
Flemming, B. W., 1981, Factors controlling sediment dispersal along the southeastern African continental margin: Marine Geology, v. 42, p. 259-277.
Fouch, T. D., T. F. Lawton, D. J. Nichols, W. D. Cashion, and W. A. Cobban, 1983, Patterns and timing of synorogenic sedimentation in Upper Cretaceous rocks of central and northeast Utah, *in* M. W. Reynolds and E. D. Dolly, eds., Mesozoic paleogeography of west-central United States, Rocky Mountain Section: Society of Economic Paleontologists and Mineralogists Rocky Mountain Paleogeography Symposium 2, p. 305-336.
Frazier, D. E., 1967, Recent deltaic deposits of the Mississippi river: their development and chronology: Transactions of the Gulf Coast Association of Geological Societies, v. 17, p. 287-315.
Frazier, D. E., 1974. Depositional episodes: their relationship to the Quaternary stratigraphic framework in the northwestern portion of the Gulf basin: Bureau of Economic Geology Geological Circular 74-1, University of Texas at Austin, 28 p.
Frazier, D. E., and A. Osanik, 1967, Recent peat deposits—Louisiana coastal plain, *in* E. C. Dapples and M. E. Hopkins, eds., Environments of coal deposition: Geological Society of America Special Paper 114, 85 p.
Galloway, W. E., 1989a, Genetic stratigraphic sequences in basin analysis I: architecture and genesis of flooding-surface bounded depositional units: AAPG Bulletin, v. 73, p. 125-142.
Galloway, W. E., 1989b, Genetic stratigraphic sequences in basin analysis II: application to northwest Gulf of Mexico Cenozoic basin: AAPG Bulletin, v. 73, p. 143-154.
Gary, M., R. McAfee, Jr., and C. L. Wolf, eds., 1972, Glossary of geology: American Geological Institute, Washington, D.C., 805 p.
Gill, J. R., and W. A. Cobban, 1966, The Red Bird section of the Upper Cretaceous Pierre Shale in Wyoming: United States Geological Survey Professional Paper 393-A, 73 p.
Gill, J. R., and W. J. Hail, Jr., 1975, Stratigraphic sections across Upper Cretaceous Mancos Shale-Mesaverde Group boundary, eastern Utah and western Colorado: Oil and Gas Investigation chart OC-68.
Goldhammer, R. K., P. A. Dunn, and L. A. Hardie, 1987, High frequency glacio-eustatic sealevel oscillations with Milankovitch characteristics recorded in Middle Triassic platform carbonates in northern Italy: American Journal of Science, v. 287, p. 853-892.
Goodwin, P. W., and E. J. Anderson,1985, Punctuated aggradational cycles: a general hypothesis of episodic stratigraphic accumulation: Journal of Geology, v. 93, p. 515-533.
Gould, H. R., 1970, The Mississippi delta complex, *in* J. P. Morgan, ed., Deltaic sedimentation: Economic Paleontologists and Mineralogists Special Publication Number 15, p. 3-31.
Grabau, A. W., 1932, Principles of stratigraphy: New York, S. G. Seiler, 1185 p.
Hale, L. A., and F. R. Van De Graaff, 1964, Cretaceous stratigraphy and facies patterns-northeastern Utah and adjacent areas, *in* E. F. Sabatka, ed., Guidebook to the geology and mineral resources of the Uinta basin: Intermountain Association of Petroleum Geologists Thirteenth Annual Field Conference, September 16-19, p. 115-138.
Hallam, A., 1984, Pre-Quaternary sea-level changes: Annual Reviews, Earth and Planetary Sciences, v. 12, p. 205-243.
Haq, B. U., J. Hardenbol, and P. R. Vail, 1987, Chronology of fluctuating sea levels since the Triassic: Science, v. 235, p. 1156-1167.
Haq, B. U., J. Hardenbol, and P. R. Vail, 1988, Mesozoic and Cenozoic chronostratigraphy and cycles of sea-level change, *in* C.K. Wilgus et al., eds., Sea-level change: an integrated approach: Society of Economic Paleontologists and Mineralogists Special Publication 42, p. 71-108.
Harms, J. C., 1966, Stratigraphic traps in a valley fill, western Nebraska: AAPG Bulletin, v. 50, p. 2119-2149.
Heezen, B. C., M. Tharp, and M. Ewing, 1959, The floors of the oceans, I. The North Atlantic: Geological Society of America Special Paper 65, 122 p.
Hubbard, R. J., 1988, Age and significance of sequence boundaries on Jurassic and Early Cretaceous rifted continental margins: AAPG Bulletin, v. 72, p. 49-72.
Jervey, M. T., 1988, Quantitative geological modeling of siliciclastic rock sequences and their seismic expressions, *in* C. K. Wilgus et al., eds., Sea level changes: an integrated approach: Society of Economic Paleontologists and Mineralogists Special Publication 42, p. 47-69.
Kamola, D. L., and J. D. Howard, 1985, Back barrier and shallow marine depositional facies, Spring Canyon Member, Blackhawk Formation: Society of Economic Paleontologists and Mineralogists Midyear Meeting Field Guides, p. 10-35 through 10-67.
Kidwell, S. M., 1989, Stratigraphic condensation of marine transgressive records: origin of major shell deposits in the Miocene of Maryland: The Journal of Geology, v. 97, p. 1-29.
Krumbein, W. C., and L. L. Sloss, 1963, Stratigraphy and Sedimentation, San Francisco, W. H. Freeman and Co., 660 p.
Loutit, T. S., J. Hardenbol, P. R. Vail, and G. R. Baum, 1988, Condensed sections: the key to age determination and correlation of continental margin sequences, *in* C. K. Wilgus et al., eds.: Society of Paleontologists and Mineralogists Special Publication 42, p. 183-213.
Mallory, W. M., ed., 1972, Atlas of the Rocky Mountain region: Rocky Mountain Association of Geologists, 331 p.
Miall, A. D., 1986, Eustatic sea level changes interpreted from seismic stratigraphy: a critique of the methodology with particular reference to the North Sea Jurassic record: AAPG Bulletin, v. 70, p. 131-137.
Middleton, G. V., 1973, Johannes Walther's law of the correlation of facies: Geological Society of America Bulletin, v. 84, p. 979-988.
Mitchum, R. M., 1977, Seismic stratigraphy and global changes of sea level, Part 1: Glossary of terms used in seismic stratigraphy, *in* C. E. Payton, ed., Seismic stratigraphy-applications to hydrocarbon exploration: AAPG Memoir 26, p. 205-212.
Mitchum, R. M., P. R. Vail, and S. Thompson, III, 1977, Seismic stratigraphy and global changes of sea level, Part 2: the depositional sequence as a basic unit for stratigraphic analysis, *in* C. E. Payton, ed., Seismic stratigraphy applications to hydrocarbon exploration: AAPG Memoir 26, p. 53-62.
Murray, G. E., 1961, Geology of the Atlantic and Gulf coastal province of North America: New York, Harper and Bros., 692 p.
Mutti, E., 1985, Turbidite systems and their relations to depositional sequences, *in* G. G. Zuffa, ed., Provenance of arenites, NATO-ASI series: Reidel Publishing Company, p. 65-93.
Mutti, E., G. P. Allen, and J. Rosell, 1984, Sigmoidal cross stratification and sigmoidal bars: depositional features diagnostic of tidal sandstones, abstract, 5th European Regional Meeting of Sedimentology: International Association of Sedimentologists, Marseille, p. 312-313.
Mutti, E., J. Rosell, G. P. Allen, F. Fonnesu, and M. Sgavetti, 1985, The Eocene Baronia tide-dominated delta-shelf system in the

Ager basin, *in* Field trip guidebook of the VI European meeting of the International Association of Sedimentologists, Lerida, Spain, excursion 13, p. 579-600.
Parkinson, N., C. Summerhayes, 1985, Synchronous global sequence boundaries: AAPG Bulletin, v. 69, p. 685-687.
Payton, C. E., ed., 1977, Seismic stratigraphy-applications to hydrocarbon exploration: AAPG Memoir 26, v. 11, 516 p.
Pfaff, B. J., 1985, Facies sequences and the evolution of fluvial sedimentation in the Castlegate Sandstone, Price Canyon, Utah: Society of Economic Paleontologists and Mineralogists Midyear Meeting Field Guides, p. 10-7 through 10-32.
Phillips, J., 1836, The geology of Yorkshire, II, The Mountain Limestone District: London, Murray, 253 p.
Pitman, W. C., III, and X. Golovchenko, 1983, The effect of sealevel change on the shelfedge and slope of passive margins, *in* D. J. Stanley and G. T. Moore, eds., The shelfbreak: critical interface on continental margins: Society of Economic Paleontologists and Mineralogists Special Publication 33, p. 41-58.
Plafker, G., 1965, Tectonic deformation associated with the 1964 Alaska earthquake: Science v. 148, p. 1675-1687.
Plafker, G., and J. C. Savage, 1970, Mechanism of the Chilean earthquake of May 21 and 22, 1960: Geological Society of America Bulletin, v. 81, p. 1001-1030.
Posamentier, H. W., and P. R. Vail, 1988, Eustatic controls on clastic deposition II-sequence and systems tract models, *in* C. K. Wilgus et al., eds., Sea-level changes: an integrated approach: Society of Economic Paleontologists and Mineralogists Special Publication 42, p. 125-154.
Posamentier, H. W., M. T. Jervey, and P. R. Vail, 1988, Eustatic controls on clastic deposition I-conceptual framework, *in* C. K. Wilgus et al., eds., Sea-level changes: an integrated approach: Society of Economic Paleontologists and Mineralogists Special Publication 42, p. 109-124.
Rainwater, E. H., 1967, Resume of Jurassic to Recent sedimentation history of Gulf of Mexico basin: Transactions of the Gulf Coast Association of Geological Societies, v. 17, p. 179-210.
Reading, H. G., 1978, Sedimentary environments and facies: New York, Elsevier Press, 557 p.
Renard, M., 1986, Pelagic carbonate chemostratigraphy (Sr, M^9, O^{18}, C^{13}): Marine Micropaleontology, v. 10, p. 117-164.
Ryer, T. A., 1983, Transgressive-regressive cycles and the occurrence of coal in some Upper Cretaceous strata of Utah: Geology, v. 11, p. 207-210.
Sarg, J. F., 1988, Carbonate sequence stratigraphy, *in* C. K. Wilgus et al., eds., Sea-level changes: an integrated approach: Society of Economic Paleontologists and Mineralogists Special Publication 42, p. 155-181.
Sears, J. D., C. B. Hunt, and T. A. Hendricks, 1941, Transgressive and regressive Cretaceous deposits in southern San Juan basin, New Mexico: U. S. Geological Survey Professional Paper 193 F, p. 101-121.
Shanley, K. W., and P. J. McCabe, 1989, Predicting fluvial architecture through sequence stratigraphy: Turonian-Campanian strata, Kaiparowits Plateau, Utah, U.S.A., abstract, Fourth International Fluvial Conference, Barcelona, Spain.
Shepard, F. P., 1973, Submarine geology, Third edition: New York, Harper and Row, 557 p.
Shurr, G. W., and J. Reskind, 1984, Stratigraphic framework of the Niobrara Formation (Upper Cretaceous) in North and South Dakota, *in* D. F. Stott and D. J. Glass, eds., The Mesozoic of middle North America: Canadian Society of Petroleum Geologists Memoir 9, p. 205-219.
Sloss, L. L., 1950, Paleozoic stratigraphy in the Montana area: AAPG Bulletin, v. 34, p. 423-451.
Sloss, L. L., 1963, Sequences in the cratonic interior of North America: Geological Society of America Bulletin, v. 74, p. 93-114.
Sloss, L. L., 1979, Global sea level change: a view from the craton, *in* J. S. Watkins et al., eds., Geological and geophysical investigations of continental margins: AAPG Memoir 29, p. 461-467.
Sloss, L. L., 1988, Forty years of sequence stratigraphy: Geological Society of America Bulletin, v. 100, p. 1661-1665.
Sloss, L. L., W. C. Krumbein, and E. C. Dapples, 1949, Integrated facies analysis, *in* C. R. Longwell, ed., Sedimentary facies-geologic history: Geological Society of America Memoir 39, p. 91-124.
Spieker, E. M., 1949, Sedimentary facies and associated diastrophism in the Upper Cretaceous of central and eastern Utah: Geological Association of America Memoir 39, p. 55-81.
Stone, W. D., 1972, Stratigraphy and exploration of the Lower Cretaceous Muddy Formation, northern Powder River basin, Wyoming and Montana: The Mountain Geologist, v. 9, p. 355-378.
Suter, J. R., and H. L. Berryhill, Jr., 1985, Late Quaternary shelf-margin deltas, Northwest Gulf of Mexico: AAPG Bulletin, v. 69, p. 77-91.
Suter, J. R., H. L. Berryhill, and S. Penland, 1987, Late Quaternary sea-level fluctuations and depositional sequences, southwest Louisiana continental shelf, *in* D. Nummedal et al., eds., Sea level fluctuation and coastal evaluation: Society of Economic Paleontologists and Mineralogists Special Publication 41, p. 199-219.
Swift, D. J. P., P. M. Hudelson, R. L. Brenner, and P. Thompson, 1987, Shelf construction in a foreland basin: storm beds, shelf sandbodies, and shelf- slope depositional sequences in the Upper Cretaceous Mesaverde Group, Book Cliffs, Utah: Sedimentology, v. 34, p. 423-457.
Thorne, J. R., and A. B. Watts, 1984, Seismic reflectors and unconformities at passive continental margins: Nature, v. 311, p. 365-368.
Udden, J. A., 1912, Geology and mineral resources of the Peoria Quadrangle, Illinois: U. S. Geological Survey Professional Paper 506, 103 p.
Vail, P. R., 1987, Seismic stratigraphy interpretation using sequence stratigraphy. Part 1: seismic stratigraphy interpretation procedure, *in* A. W. Bally, ed., Atlas of seismic stratigraphy, v. 1: AAPG Studies in Geology 27, p. 1-10.
Vail, P. R., R. M. Mitchum, and S. Thompson, III, 1977, Seismic stratigraphy and global changes of sea level, part 3: relative changes of sea level from coastal onlap, *in* C. W. Payton, ed., Seismic stratigraphy applications to hydrocarbon exploration: AAPG Memoir 26, p. 63-97.
Vail, P. R., R. M. Mitchum, T. H. Shipley, and R. T. Buffler, 1980, Unconformities in the North Atlantic: Philosophical Transactions of the Royal Society of London, A 294, p. 137-155.
Vail, P. R., and R. G. Todd, 1981, North Sea Jurassic unconformities, chronostratigraphy and sea-level changes from seismic stratigraphy, Proceedings of the Petroleum Geology Continental Shelf, Northwest Europe, p. 216-235.
Vail, P. R., J. Hardenbol, and R. G. Todd, 1984, Jurassic unconformities, chronostratigraphy and sea-level changes from seismic stratigraphy and biostratigraphy, *in* J. S. Schlee, ed., Inter-regional unconformities and hydrocarbon accumulation: AAPG Memoir 36, p. 129-144.
Van De Graaff, F. R., 1970, Depositional environments and petrology of the Castlegate Sandstone: University of Missouri, Columbia, Ph. D. dissertation, 120 p.
Van Wagoner, J. C., 1985, Reservoir facies distribution as controlled by sea-level change, abstract: Society of Economic Paleontologists and Mineralogists Mid-Year Meeting, Golden, Colorado, August 11-14, p. 91-92.
Van Wagoner, J. C., H. W. Posamentier, R. M. Mitchum, P. R. Vail, J. F. Sarg, T. S. Loutit, and J. Hardenbol, 1988, An overview of sequence stratigraphy and key definitions, *in* C. W. Wilgus et al., eds., Sea level changes: an integrated approach: Society of Economic Paleontologists and Mineralogists Special Publication 42, p. 39-45.
Van Wagoner, J. C., and R. M. Mitchum, 1989, High-frequency sequences and their stacking patterns, abstract: 28th International Geological Congress, Washington, D. C., July 9-19, p. 3-284.
Walker, R. G., 1984, General introduction: facies, facies sequences and facies models, *in* R. G. Walker, ed., Facies Models, second edition: Geological Society of Canada, Geoscience Canada, Reprint Series 1, p. 1-9.
Walther, J., 1894, Einleitung in die Geologie als historiche Wissenschaft: Jena, Verlag von Gustav Fisher, 3 vols., p. 987-993.
Wanless, H. R., 1950, Late Paleozoic cycles of sedimentation in the United States, 18th International Geological Congress: London, 1948, Report 4, p. 17-28.
Watts, A. B., 1982, Tectonic subsidence, flexure, and global changes of sea level: Nature, v. 297, p. 469-474.
Weimer, R. J., 1983, Relation of unconformities, tectonism, and sea-level changes, Cretaceous of the Denver basin and adjacent

areas, *in* M. W. Reynolds and E. D. Dolly, eds., Mesozoic paleogeography of west-central United States: Rocky Mountain Section, Society of Economic Paleontologists and Mineralogists Rocky Mountain Paleogeography Symposium 2, p. 359-376.

Weimer, R. J., 1984, Relations of unconformities, tectonics, and sea-level changes, Cretaceous of western interior U.S.A., *in* J. S. Schlee, ed., Interregional unconformities and hydrocarbon accumulation: AAPG Memoir 36, p. 7-35.

Weimer, R. J., 1988, Record of sea-level changes, Cretaceous of western interior, U. S. A., *in* C. K. Wilgus et al., eds., Sea-level changes: an integrated approach: Society of Economic Paleontologists and Mineralogists Special Publication 42, p. 285-288.

Weller, J. M., 1930, Cyclical sedimentation of the Pennsylvanian period and its significance: Journal of Geology, v. 38, p. 97-135.

Wheeler, H. E., 1958, Time stratigraphy: AAPG Bulletin, v. 42, p. 1047-1063.

Williams, D. G., 1984, Correlation of Pleistocene marine sediments of the Gulf of Mexico and other basins using oxygen isotope stratigraphy, *in* N. Healy-Williams, ed., Principles of Pleistocene stratigraphy applied to the Gulf of Mexico: International Human Resources Development Corporation, Boston, p. 65-118.

Wilson, J. L., 1975, Carbonate facies in geologic history: New York, Springer-Verlag, 471 p.

Wright, R., 1986, Cycle stratigraphy as a paleogeographic tool: Point Lookout Sandstone, southeastern San Juan basin, New Mexico: Geological Society of America Bulletin, v. 97, p. 661-673.

Young, R. G., 1955, Sedimentary facies and intertonguing in the Upper Cretaceous of the Book Cliffs, Utah-Colorado: Geological Society of America Bulletin, v. 66, p. 177-202.